My Colourful Day

Illustrations by

Amelia Rosato

EGMONT
children's books

First published in Great Britain 2000 by Egmont Children's Books Limited
239 Kensington High Street, London W8 6SA
Illustrated by Amelia Rosato
Text by Laura Dollin. Designed by Suzanne Cocks.
Copyright © 2000 Egmont Children's Books Limited
ISBN 0 7497 4187 2
Printed in Italy

1 3 5 7 9 10 8 6 4 2

 Good morning! Time to get out of bed.
Nita's favourite pyjamas are **red!**

Yum-yum-yummy inside her tummy,
Nita's breakfast is very scrummy!

Look! Some **yellow** trousers to wear.
Nita can **reach** them from her chair.

Up-up-up-and-up, do not stop,
Blue bricks all the way to the top!

Round-and-round-and-round-and-round it goes...

Today we are washing lots of **green** clothes.

Black boots! Pull them on,
Heeeeeave-ho!
Then out to the garden we can go.

Dig- dig- dig, an **orange** bucket and spade,
Look at the sand-castle Nita has made!

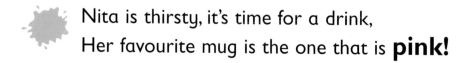

Nita is thirsty, it's time for a drink,
Her favourite mug is the one that is **pink!**

Splish-*splash*, lots of bubbles,
fluffy and **white,**
Then a cosy, warm towel, all wrapped up tight!

Ssshhhhhh!
Now Nita is asleep in bed,
With **brown** teddy sleeping beside her head.